My Favorite Book

Won't you come along?

Good Will Publishers, Inc.

Won't you come along?

Won't you come along with us as we enter the colorful world of childhood. It is a world where basic character traits such as respect of self and others, personal responsibility, honesty, obedience, courtesy, thoughtfulness and gratitude are first learned and applied in the daily lives of the little ones who are so dear to us. It is also the world in which Family, School and Community begin to function cooperatively to instill in children positive standards of conduct, the standards we hope they will carry with them throughout their lives. *My Favorite Book* is a collection of beautifully illustrated verses about these basic standards. It is designed to be used as a springboard for discussion between parent and child and between teacher and child.

During the primary school years, a child's world begins to expand beyond the family. The school and community are now becoming important parts of the child's life. *My Favorite Book* celebrates family, school and community life in a very positive way. It celebrates the educational process, friendship, close family ties, good citizenship and doing the right thing.

Reading can and should be one of the positive experiences that help our children grow into maturity. So won't you come along with us as we explore in delightful verse and charming art, the value oriented world of our children.

The friends in your community who sponsor *My Favorite Book* are pleased to be able to play a role in providing a reading experience about basic values. Please let these thoughtful neighbors know when you have received a copy of the book.

My Favorite Book is illustrated by Jean Goebel.

A message to the children from the artist
"This book is all about being a 'Gold Star person.'
See if you can find the gold star I've hidden on each illustrated page."

Education Consultant
Gerald Healy, M.A.

3/97

My Favorite Book

Sponsored by

**May This Always Be
Your Favorite Book**

This is
My Favorite Book.

This is the way I look.

I am____ years old.

_____

This is the way I write my name.

_____

This is where I live.

These are the names of my Family Members

These are the names
of some of my Friends

_____

_____

_____

_____

_____

This is the name of my
Principal

_____

These are the names
of my Teachers

_____

_____

_____

_____

Obeying the Rules at Home and at School

At our house there is a rule
that we must obey.
The rule is that we always do
whatever Mom or Dad may say.

So in school
   we should always do
what our teacher asks.
That is the way
   to show our manners
and be an obedient class.

The Work We All Do

Every morning
when the sun comes up
the people in our town
get ready for work.

Some are nurses
and some sell cars.
My dad knows a scientist
who studies the stars.

Salespeople and dentists
and firefighters too,
are people we count on
for the work they do.

There are merchants and ministers
and librarians too.
We should all work hard
at the jobs we do.

Even kids like me
have jobs to get done,
because work is important
for the old *and* the young.

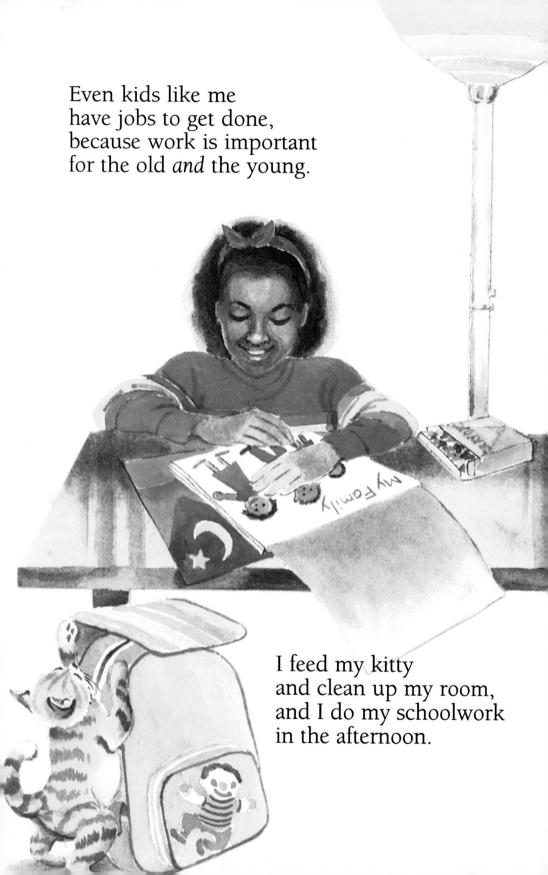

I feed my kitty
and clean up my room,
and I do my schoolwork
in the afternoon.

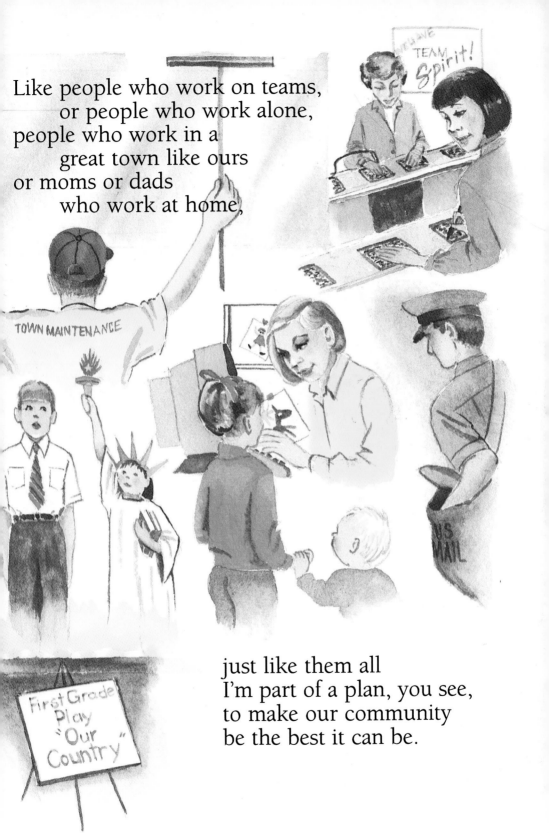

Like people who work on teams,
    or people who work alone,
people who work in a
    great town like ours
or moms or dads
    who work at home,

just like them all
I'm part of a plan, you see,
to make our community
be the best it can be.

Learning to Read

Learning to read is lots of fun.
We are learning our letters one by one.
Each letter has a sound,
and sounds are the keys.

They unlock the door
to our ABC's.
Words can be beautiful,
don't you agree?
I like CAT and YES
and YOU and ME.

Words Can Be Beautiful

Merrily

Barbara Ferreri

Learn-ing to read is lots of fun,———
Let-ters have sounds and sounds are keys un-

Learn-ing our let - ters one by one,
lock-ing the door to our A B C's,

REFRAIN

Words can be beau - ti - ful, don't you a - gree?
Words can be beau - ti - ful, don't you a - gree?

I like "CAT" and "YES" and "SEE".
I like "THEM" and "YOU" and "ME"!

thank you me

right mom

cat book know

responsible brother

sister uncle

friend grandpa
grandma

aunt

dad

play love

apple

you please we

yes happy

I Can Be Responsible

My room is a mess! My room is a mess!
I don't know what to do!
My parents won't let me go out and play
til my bedroom looks like new!

Maybe I could find my clean socks
and put them in a drawer,
and then all my dirty clothes
could be picked up off the floor.

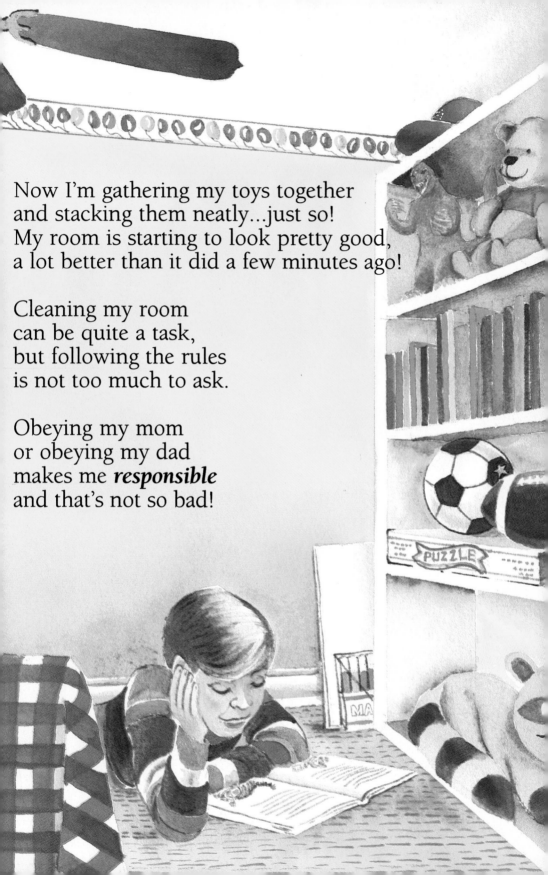

Now I'm gathering my toys together
and stacking them neatly...just so!
My room is starting to look pretty good,
a lot better than it did a few minutes ago!

Cleaning my room
can be quite a task,
but following the rules
is not too much to ask.

Obeying my mom
or obeying my dad
makes me *responsible*
and that's not so bad!

Some Things Are Dangerous

I saw some big blue bottles
below our kitchen sink.
I just wanted something to play with,
I guess I didn't think

that some bottles are dangerous
and could hurt a kid, you see.
"Poison" Mom calls it,
and she keeps it away from me.

Medicine that the grownups take,
and the stuff that cleans the floors,
many things can hurt us kids
behind our cabinet doors.

So before I play with bottles,
I ask a grown up, not a little girl or boy.
Just because something looks like fun
doesn't mean it is a toy.

My Family

Grandma has a scrapbook
with pictures on every page,
pictures of Mom when she was little like me,
and cousins of every age.

In it are pictures of dear old friends.
Friends can be like family we say,

because family are those
who care very much,
and are close in a special way.

Like the older lady
Mom called Aunt Lea
who stacked her hair up in a bun.
She loved to bake cookies
with big chocolate chunks
then watch all the children have fun!

Happy is the family pet,
a family member most true.
His hair is curly and stringy and wild,
and on Grandma's shoes
    he loves to chew!

On holidays my family gets bigger
with aunts and uncles
   and cousins and friends.
So, if I am asked the size of my family,
I say, "Well, it just depends!"

"Thank You" Is The Thing To Say

My Mom and I took a trip to town
She had some errands to run.
We went to the bank and the drugstore too
I thought we would never be done!

When we stopped at the bank Mrs. Jenson said,
"What a big boy you have become.
I've got some lollipops here in my drawer,
would you like me to give you one?"

The candy was so delicious and sweet
   and sticky to the touch.
Because it was such a nice thing to do,
   I said, "Thank you very much!"

At the drugstore I saw Mr. Thomason.
He has worked there a long, long time.
He worked there when my daddy was little.
Mom says he is generous and kind.

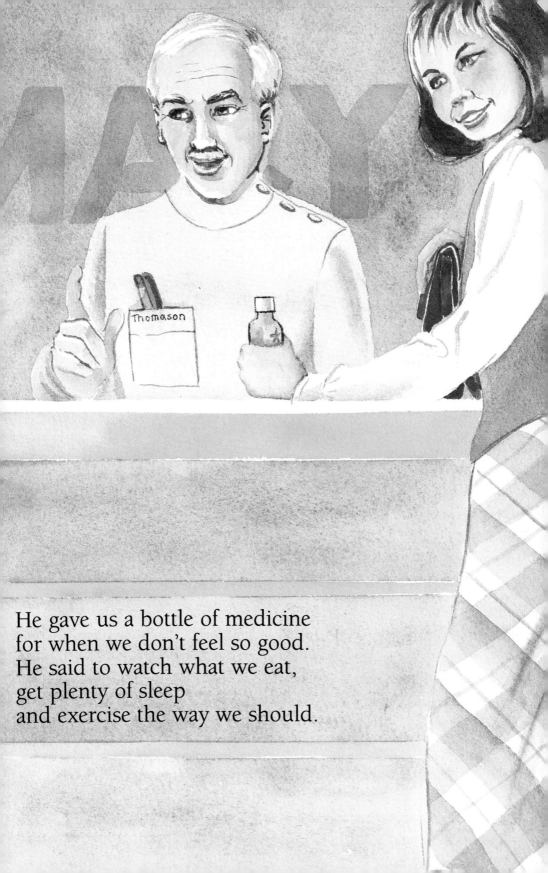

He gave us a bottle of medicine
for when we don't feel so good.
He said to watch what we eat,
get plenty of sleep
and exercise the way we should.

Some people in our neighborhood
are people who like being nice.
If you ever need their help at all,
you don't even have to ask twice!

So "Thank you!" is the thing to say,
of that there is no doubt.
"Thank you very much, indeed,"
when neighbors help us out.

When I grow up,
I would like to be
as good to my friends
    and neighbors
as they have been to me.

Learning Right and Wrong

Right is doing chores at home.

Wrong is not telling the truth.

Right is following the rules of our class.

Wrong is hitting best friend Ruth.

Right is helping a friend who is hurt.

Wrong is to not even bother.

Right is obeying Principal and Teacher.

Wrong is ignoring Sister or Brother.

Right is recycling
our newspapers and cans.

Wrong is littering
our highways and lands.

Wrong is hurting others
by saying things we should not,

or forgetting "please" and "thank you,"
words we should say a lot.

Let us be obedient,
    thoughtful and kind,
honest and responsible
    all of the time.

Let us *always* try to do what is right
    and *never* do what is wrong.
Let us respect others
    as well as ourselves.
Won't you come along?